FOREIGN
LANGUAGE COURSES

# Power-Glide
# Children's Spanish Level II

*Activity Book*

by

Robert W. Blair

This product would not have been possible without the assistance of many people. The help of those mentioned below was invaluable.

Editorial, Design and Production Staff

Instructional Design: Robert Blair, Ph.D.

Project Coordinator: James Blair

Development Manager: David Higginbotham

Story Writer: Natalie Prado

Cover Design: Guy Francis

Contributing Editors: Gretchen Hilton, Emily Spackman, Phillip Morris

Audios Voices: Dell Blair, Luke Drake, Robert Blair, Rebeca Witham, Freddy Gómez, Miriam Ruiz

Illustrator: Apryl Robertson

Translators: Phillip Morris, Robert Blair

Musicians: Geoff Groberg, Rob Fulkerson

Audio Recording, Editing and Mixing: Rob Fulkerson

Power-Glide Foreign Language Courses
1682 W 820 N, Provo, UT 84601
(4/01)

# Contents

Introduction . . . . . . . . . . . . . . . . . . . . . . . . . . . . . . . . . . . . . . . . . . . . . . . . . . . . . . . . . . .5

The Adventure Begins . . . . . . . . . . . . . . . . . . . . . . . . . . . . . . . . . . . . . . . . . . . . . . . . .8

Hola Lisa . . . . . . . . . . . . . . . . . . . . . . . . . . . . . . . . . . . . . . . . . . . . . . . . . . . . . . . . . .11

No Sé Cuándo . . . . . . . . . . . . . . . . . . . . . . . . . . . . . . . . . . . . . . . . . . . . . . . . . . . . . .14

The Three Pigs I

   *Scatter Chart* . . . . . . . . . . . . . . . . . . . . . . . . . . . . . . . . . . . . . . . . . . . . . . . . . . . .17

   *Match and Learn* . . . . . . . . . . . . . . . . . . . . . . . . . . . . . . . . . . . . . . . . . . . . . . . . .19

   *Diglot Weave* . . . . . . . . . . . . . . . . . . . . . . . . . . . . . . . . . . . . . . . . . . . . . . . . . . . .23

   *Review Questions* . . . . . . . . . . . . . . . . . . . . . . . . . . . . . . . . . . . . . . . . . . . . . . . . .26

The Three Pigs II

   *Scatter Chart* . . . . . . . . . . . . . . . . . . . . . . . . . . . . . . . . . . . . . . . . . . . . . . . . . . . .28

   *Match and Learn* . . . . . . . . . . . . . . . . . . . . . . . . . . . . . . . . . . . . . . . . . . . . . . . . .30

   *Diglot Weave* . . . . . . . . . . . . . . . . . . . . . . . . . . . . . . . . . . . . . . . . . . . . . . . . . . . .33

   *Story Telling* . . . . . . . . . . . . . . . . . . . . . . . . . . . . . . . . . . . . . . . . . . . . . . . . . . . .36

Word Puzzle 1 . . . . . . . . . . . . . . . . . . . . . . . . . . . . . . . . . . . . . . . . . . . . . . . . . . . . . . .37

A Circus Act

   *Horseshoe Story* . . . . . . . . . . . . . . . . . . . . . . . . . . . . . . . . . . . . . . . . . . . . . . . . . .40

   *Match and Learn* . . . . . . . . . . . . . . . . . . . . . . . . . . . . . . . . . . . . . . . . . . . . . . . . .41

   *Horseshoe Story Review* . . . . . . . . . . . . . . . . . . . . . . . . . . . . . . . . . . . . . . . . . . .44

Word Puzzle 2 . . . . . . . . . . . . . . . . . . . . . . . . . . . . . . . . . . . . . . . . . . . . . . . . . . . . . . .37

Test 1 . . . . . . . . . . . . . . . . . . . . . . . . . . . . . . . . . . . . . . . . . . . . . . . . . . . . . . . . . . . . . .47

Answer Key . . . . . . . . . . . . . . . . . . . . . . . . . . . . . . . . . . . . . . . . . . . . . . . . . . . . . . . . .50

The Adventure Continues . . . . . . . . . . . . . . . . . . . . . . . . . . . . . . . . . . . . . . . . . . . . . .52

Uno, dos, tres niñitos . . . . . . . . . . . . . . . . . . . . . . . . . . . . . . . . . . . . . . . . . . . . . . . . . .54

Abuelito . . . . . . . . . . . . . . . . . . . . . . . . . . . . . . . . . . . . . . . . . . . . . . . . . . . . . . . . . . . .57

Chicken Little I

   *Scatter Chart* . . . . . . . . . . . . . . . . . . . . . . . . . . . . . . . . . . . . . . . . . . . . . . . . . . . .59

   *Match and Learn* . . . . . . . . . . . . . . . . . . . . . . . . . . . . . . . . . . . . . . . . . . . . . . . . .61

   *Diglot Weave* . . . . . . . . . . . . . . . . . . . . . . . . . . . . . . . . . . . . . . . . . . . . . . . . . . . .64

   *Review Questions* . . . . . . . . . . . . . . . . . . . . . . . . . . . . . . . . . . . . . . . . . . . . . . . . .67

The Three Pigs II

   *Scatter Chart* . . . . . . . . . . . . . . . . . . . . . . . . . . . . . . . . . . . . . . . . . . . . . . . . . . . .69

   *Match and Learn* . . . . . . . . . . . . . . . . . . . . . . . . . . . . . . . . . . . . . . . . . . . . . . . . .70

   *Diglot Weave* . . . . . . . . . . . . . . . . . . . . . . . . . . . . . . . . . . . . . . . . . . . . . . . . . . . .72

   *Story Telling* . . . . . . . . . . . . . . . . . . . . . . . . . . . . . . . . . . . . . . . . . . . . . . . . . . . .76

Word Puzzle 3 . . . . . . . . . . . . . . . . . . . . . . . . . . . . . . . . . . . . . . . . . . . . . . . . . . . . . . .77

The Mantis and The Butterfly

   *Horseshoe Story* . . . . . . . . . . . . . . . . . . . . . . . . . . . . . . . . . . . . . . . . . . . . . . . . . .79

   *Match and Learn* . . . . . . . . . . . . . . . . . . . . . . . . . . . . . . . . . . . . . . . . . . . . . . . . .80

   *Horseshoe Story Review* . . . . . . . . . . . . . . . . . . . . . . . . . . . . . . . . . . . . . . . . . . .82

Word Puzzle 4 . . . . . . . . . . . . . . . . . . . . . . . . . . . . . . . . . . . . . . . . . . . . . . . . . . . . . . .84

Final Word Puzzle . . . . . . . . . . . . . . . . . . . . . . . . . . . . . . . . . . . . . . . . . . . . . . . . . . . .87

Test 2 . . . . . . . . . . . . . . . . . . . . . . . . . . . . . . . . . . . . . . . . . . . . . . . . . . . . . . . . . . . . . .90

Answer Key . . . . . . . . . . . . . . . . . . . . . . . . . . . . . . . . . . . . . . . . . . . . . . . . . . . . . . . . .92

# A Note to Parents

## Basic Course Objectives

The major goal of this course is to keep children excited about communicating in another language. The adventure story, the variety of activities, and the simplified teaching methods employed in the course are all designed to make learning interesting and fun.

This course is primarily for children 2nd through 4th grade. Course activities are designed specifically with these learners in mind and include matching games, story telling, speaking, drawing, creative and deductive thinking, acting, and guessing—all things which children do for fun!

Ultimately, children who complete the course can expect to understand an impressive amount of Spanish, including common Spanish phrases, complete Spanish sentences, Spanish numbers, rhymes, and questions. They will also be able to understand stories told all or mostly in Spanish, to retell these stories themselves using Spanish, and to make up stories of their own using words and sentence patterns they have learned.

Children who complete the course will be well prepared to continue learning with our other Spanish courses, and they will have the foundation that will make learning at that level just as fun and interesting, albeit more challenging, than in this course.

## Teaching Techniques

This course allows your children to learn by doing: to learn through enjoyable experiences. The idea is to put the experience first and the explanation after. This is important to note because it is directly opposite to how teaching—and especially foreign language teaching—is traditionally done. Typically foreign language teachers spend the majority of their time explaining complex grammar and syntax rules, and drilling students on vocabulary. In this traditional mode, rules and lists come first and experience comes last. Learning experientially, on the other hand, simulates the natural language acquisition process of children.

When children learn their native languages apparently effortlessly in early childhood, it is not through the study of grammar rules and vocabulary lists. Rather, they learn the words for things around them simply by listening to others, and they intuitively grasp an amazing amount of grammar and syntax in the same way. By using activities that simulate natural language acquisition, it is not only possible, but normal for children to learn a new language quickly and enjoy doing it!

Specifically, this course motivates your children to learn Spanish by providing learning experiences in the form of matching games, story telling exercises, drawing exercises, singing and acting, and other fun activities aimed at developing functional language comprehension and speaking ability. These activities contrast markedly with the exercises in more traditional courses, which tend to focus exclusively on learning some vocabulary, or on understanding very simple Spanish sentences, without extending learning to the point of actually understanding and speaking the language. The language your children will acquire through this course will be more useful to them than language learned through traditional approaches, because knowledge gained in fun, rather than stressful, ways is much easier for children to retain and much more natural for them to use themselves.

## Using the Course

This course is carefully designed so that it can be used either by children working primarily on their own or by parents and children working closely together. Complete instructions, simple enough to be easily followed by children, are included on the audios. Parents or other adults can enhance the course significantly by acting as facilitators: reviewing instructions, encouraging creativity and course participation, providing frequent opportunities for children to display what they have learned, rewarding effort and accomplishment, and providing enthusiasm. Keep in mind that much of the real learning takes place as you interact with your children during and after the course learning experiences.

Perhaps the most important of the above ways parents can help their children is to give them an audience for their new skills. In order to facilitate this invaluable help, we have added a new feature to the Children's Level II Spanish Course. At the end of each activity or story we have included suggestions for a Performance Challenge. One goal of Power-Glide courses is to teach students to produce the target language creatively and independently. The new Performance Challenge feature will help children do just that. These additional exercises will increase your child's fluency, pronunciation, and confidence in the target language, as well as give you the opportunity to be directly involved in the learning process. Encourage your children to use as much Spanish as possible and give them the audience they need to perform for. Remind your students not to worry about mistakes. Rather, encourage them to review any words they may struggle with and make sure they feel comfortable with the current material before moving to the next lesson.

Using the resources provided in the course book and on the audios, an adult learning facilitator does not need to know Spanish or how to teach it in order to be a great learning partner. In fact, one of the most enjoyable and effective ways to learn is together, as a team.

Parents or other adults who know Spanish can, of course, supplement the materials in this course very effectively. A proficient bilingual teacher could, for example: (1) help children learn additional vocabulary by putting several objects on table and asking and answering questions about them, such as "What is this?" or "Where is the _____?", and so on; (2) create on-the-spot diglot-weave stories by reading illustrated children's books such as Silverstein's *Are You My Mother?*, putting key words (picturable nouns) into Spanish, and asking questions about the story or its pictures partly or completely in Spanish; (3) involve children in making and doing things (such as making a paper airplane or finding a hidden object) giving instructions all or partly in Spanish.

We have added another new feature to this course that will make it easier to use. For each audio track, you will see a CD icon that includes the CD number and the track number. This will help you to easily find your place from lesson to lesson.

## Benefits of Second Language Acquisition

Learning a second language has many benefits. Besides the obvious value of being able to understand and communicate with others, research in the United States and Canada in the 1970s and '80s has shown that learning a second language gives children a distinct advantage in general school subject areas. Seeing linguistic and cultural contrasts as they acquire a second language, children gain insight not only into the new language and cultures, but into their own language and culture as well.

Furthermore, a considerable amount of research has shown that learning a second language in childhood helps children learn to read and write their native language. Quite possibly the best phonics training a child can receive is to learn a language like Spanish, because Spanish spelling is quite phonetic: when one knows Spanish, the spelling of a Spanish word tells him or her how to pronounce it, and (with few exceptions) the sound of a Spanish word tells him or her how to spell it. This carries over to English and helps children intuitively understand how language works.

## Our Goal

Our goal at Power-Glide is to change the way the U.S. studies language. We want to produce foreign language speakers, not just studiers. This Children's Level II Spanish Course effectively continues the road to speaking Spanish. We hope you and your children will find delight in the ongoing adventure of learning another language.

# The Adventure Begins

## (Yucatán)

 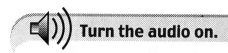

Track 1

**Narrator:** Monday, 11 a.m. You peer out of the window of the car as your family pulls up to the cozy little cottage where your Grandpa Glen has been staying. It is incredible that you are finally here, in Progreso, in Yucatán, for the first time in your life. Last week you didn't even know where Yucatán was! You only knew that your Grandpa Glen had gone there to study Mexican and Mayan folklore. When your parents decided to come down for a couple of weeks to help him with his research, you were so excited! It was a wonderful opportunity to see a new country and to practice your Spanish. Your parents seem concerned. A man who has been standing and watching you all from the yard next door approaches your parents and begins to speak with your parents in Spanish. There is something about the neighbor that you don't like, but you're not sure what it is.

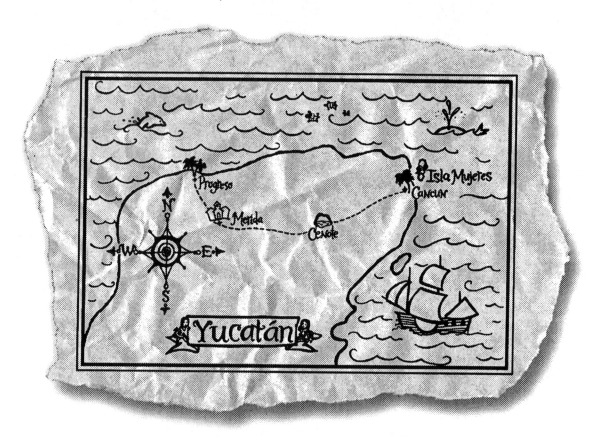

**Tony:** Lisa, can you tell what they're saying?

**Lisa:** I'm not sure, Tony.

**Malo:** ¿Abuelito Glen? Él no está. Se fue hace algunos días.

**Tony:** They must be talking about our grandpa, I heard him say "Glen."

**Lisa:** I hope everything is all right.

**Narrator:** Your parents come back and explain that this man, Malo, is your grandpa's next door neighbor. Grandpa Glen apparently had to leave town unexpectedly, and Malo had been picking up his mail for him. He also said that your distant cousin Marcela had been visiting Grandpa Glen from Valladolid, to help him with some Spanish translations.

**Lisa:** That's strange. I wonder where Grandpa Glen has gone.

**Tony:** There's something funny going on here. I know it.

**Lisa:** Well, what are we supposed to do about it?

**Narrator:** Your parents seem worried as well. The neighbor goes back over to his yard, where he is gardening. Just then, a postman comes up and hands some letters to your parents. You parents look through the letters and find one from Grandpa Glen! They open it and read it aloud.

**Grandpa Glen's Letter:** My Dear Family: I write to you out of desperation. This adventure started a couple of weeks ago. As I was doing my research, I came across the hidden diary of the notorious 17th century pirate Don Diego de Consuelo. In the diary, he mentions that he left a trail of clues, starting right here in Progreso, to mark where he had hidden some of his most precious treasure. It was not until I was well into my search that I became aware that someone had discovered my plan and was trying to sabotage it. I will need your help if I am going to succeed in finding the treasure! I cannot fail to warn you that this adventure could be dangerous. You'd have to learn a lot of Spanish, and use all your courage and intelligence to track down the clues to the treasure. Now, you may not know all the Spanish in the stories and puzzles you will encounter. All you really need to do is try and understand everything you can. If you follow my instructions, everything will start to make sense. You don't need to know everything the first time you find a new clue, that comes with time and practice. For right now, unfortunately, it is too risky for me to tell you where I am. But, I hid something at the house that you can use to find me. I hid it very well. In order to find it, you must use the poem I taught you once: "No Sé Cuándo." You absolutely must find me before noon on Thursday, or I will be forced to continue my search without you. I can wait no longer. One last note: there is one person I know I can trust. She's the granddaughter of my cousin. She lives in Valladolid. Her name is Marcela. If you can find her, she will be able to help you. It is crucially important that you begin your search immediately. Don't worry about me; I'm o.k., but without your help I will doubtless fail in my quest. Be brave. Your Grandpa, Glen.

**Narrator:** Needless to say, you and your parents are very concerned about your grandpa. Your father says that if your grandpa is in trouble, it wouldn't do any good to go wandering around the country looking for him. Instead, he decides to alert the authorities and go speak to the other people in the neighborhood.

**Lisa:** But, Dad! What can we do to help?

**Tony:** Yeah, we want to find Grandpa Glen, too. Is it okay if we try to find the clues?

**Narrator:** Your parents seem a little bit nervous. They realize that Grandpa Glen could use your help. You promise to be careful, and they say you may search around as long as you keep within sight of Grandpa's house. You promise. When your parents go inside the house to make some phone calls, you go over the letter again, and another piece of paper falls out.

**Tony:** What's this? It looks like some sort of puzzle.

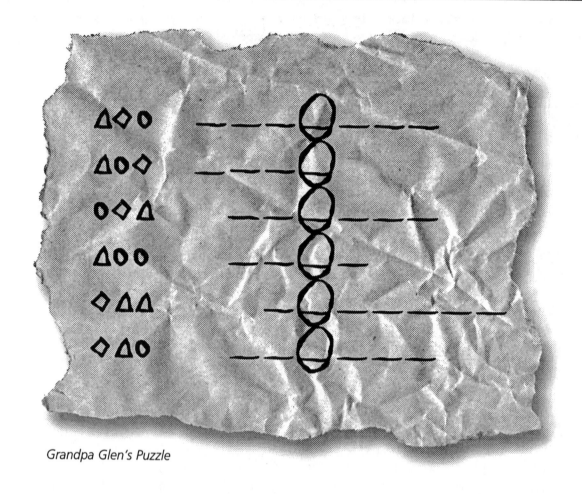

*Grandpa Glen's Puzzle*

 **Turn the audio off.**

## PERFORMANCE CHALLENGE:

Do you know where Yucatán is? Find a map of the world, an encyclopedia, or a globe and locate Yucatán.

# Hola Lisa

*(Ditties)*

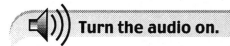 **Turn the audio on.**

*Track 2*

**Lisa:** Well, it sounds like the fist thing we should do is go and speak to Marcela. I guess we need to go and ask that neighbor, Malo, where she is.

**Tony:** Yeah, you're right. How do we begin?

**Lisa:** Don't you remember? We begin by saying "hola," like in that song, "Hola Lisa."

**Tony:** That's right! I remember. It started out like this:

| | |
|---|---|
| Hola, Lisa, | *(Hello, Lisa,)* |
| Hola, Lisa, | *(Hello, Lisa,)* |
| Hola, Lisa, | *(Hello, Lisa,)* |
| Me alegro verte hoy. | *(I am happy to see you today.)* |
| | |
| Chao pues, Lisa, | *(Goodbye then, Lisa,)* |
| Chao pues, Lisa, | *(Goodbye then, Lisa,)* |
| Chao pues, Lisa, | *(Goodbye then, Lisa,)* |
| Y que te vaya bien. | *(And take care.)* |
| ¡Hasta mañana! | *(Until Tomorrow!)* |

**Lisa:** That's right. Let's sing those through.

**Narrator:** Make sure you sing along too!

**Tony & Lisa:**

| | |
|---|---|
| Hola, Lisa, | *(Hello, Lisa,)* |
| Hola, Lisa, | *(Hello, Lisa,)* |
| Hola, Lisa, | *(Hello, Lisa,)* |
| Me alegro verte hoy. | *(I am happy to see you today.)* |
| | |
| Chao pues, Lisa, | *(Goodbye then, Lisa,)* |
| Chao pues, Lisa, | *(Goodbye then, Lisa,)* |
| Chao pues, Lisa, | *(Goodbye then, Lisa,)* |

| | |
|---|---|
| Y que te vaya bien. | *(And take care.)* |
| ¡Hasta mañana! | *(Until Tomorrow!)* |

**Lisa:** Great. I remember the next verse. It went like this.

| | |
|---|---|
| Hola, Tony, | *(Hello, Tony,)* |
| Hola, Tony, | *(Hello, Tony,)* |
| Hola, Tony, | *(Hello, Tony,)* |
| ¿Y como está usted? | *(And how are you?)* |

| | |
|---|---|
| Muy bien, gracias, | *(Very well, thank you,)* |
| Muy bien, gracias, | *(Very well, thank you,)* |
| Muy bien, gracias, | *(Very well, thank you,)* |
| Estoy bastante bien. | *(I am doing well.)* |
| ¡Hasta luego! | *(See you later!)* |

Want to see if we can sing those verses together?

**Tony:** Yeah.

**Narrator:** Don't forget to sing along!

**Tony & Lisa:**

| | |
|---|---|
| Hola, Tony, | *(Hello, Tony,)* |
| Hola, Tony, | *(Hello, Tony,)* |
| Hola, Tony, | *(Hello, Tony,)* |
| ¿Y como está usted? | *(And how are you?)* |

| | |
|---|---|
| Muy bien, gracias, | *(Very well, thank you,)* |
| Muy bien, gracias, | *(Very well, thank you,)* |
| Muy bien, gracias, | *(Very well, thank you,)* |
| Estoy bastante bien. | *(I am doing well.)* |
| ¡Hasta luego! | *(See you later!)* |

**Lisa:** Hey, we're doing really good.

**Tony:** Yeah. Do you think that we can sing the whole thing?

**Narrator:** Sure you can. Go ahead.

**Tony & Lisa:**

| | |
|---|---|
| Hola, Lisa, | *(Hello, Lisa,)* |
| Hola, Lisa, | *(Hello, Lisa,)* |
| Hola, Lisa, | *(Hello, Lisa,)* |
| Me alegro verte hoy. | *(I am happy to see you today.)* |
| | |
| Chao pues, Lisa, | *(Goodbye then, Lisa,)* |
| Chao pues, Lisa, | *(Goodbye then, Lisa,)* |
| Chao pues, Lisa, | *(Goodbye then, Lisa,)* |
| Y que te vaya bien. | *(And take care.)* |
| ¡Hasta mañana! | *(Until Tomorrow!)* |
| | |
| Hola, Tony, | *(Hello, Tony,)* |
| Hola, Tony, | *(Hello, Tony,)* |
| Hola, Tony, | *(Hello, Tony,)* |
| ¿Y como está usted? | *(And how are you?)* |
| | |
| Muy bien, gracias, | *(Very well, thank you,)* |
| Muy bien, gracias, | *(Very well, thank you,)* |
| Muy bien, gracias, | *(Very well, thank you,)* |
| Estoy bastante bien. | *(I am doing well.)* |
| ¡Hasta luego! | *(See you later!)* |

**Lisa:** Great!

 **Turn the audio off.**

## PERFORMANCE CHALLENGE:

Now that you have learned a new song, share your Spanish with a parent, friend, or one of your brothers or sisters by teaching them the song. Remember to teach it in Spanish and then translate the words into English if your partner does not understand Spanish.

# No Sé Cuándo

*(Ditties)*

 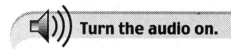

**Turn the audio on.**

*Track 3*

**Narrator:** Monday, 1 p.m.

**Lisa:** So, should we go and speak to Malo?

**Tony:** No. It looks like he's gone back inside his house. I guess we should find that "something special" that Grandpa hid first. It might be hard to find.

**Lisa:** Yeah, you're right. It could be anywhere around the house. Remember, he told us we would need the poem "No Sé Cuándo."

**Narrator:** You both begin to look.

**Tony:** Hey! Come over here! Look at this!

**Lisa:** What? What is it?

**Tony:** Look at this tree. It has a word painted on it.

**Lisa:** How strange. What does it say?

**Tony:** It says, "cuándo."

**Lisa:** Perfect! It must be a clue.

**Tony:** But now what? How does the rest of the poem go?

**Lisa:** Don't you remember? It was the song that Grandpa taught us so that we could say that we didn't know things. The first verse went like this:

| | |
|---|---|
| No sé cuándo. | *(I don't know when)* |
| No sé quién. | *(I don't know who)* |
| No sé nada | *(I don't know anything)* |
| Muy bien. | *(Very well.)* |

Okay, let's say that part together.

**Narrator:** Don't forget to sing along.

**Tony & Lisa:**

| | |
|---|---|
| No sé cuándo. | *(I don't know when)* |
| No sé quién. | *(I don't know who)* |
| No sé nada | *(I don't know anything)* |

|  |  |
|---|---|
| Muy bien. | (Very well.) |

**Tony:** Great! I remember the second verse now. It went:

|  |  |
|---|---|
| No sé cómo. | (I don't know how.) |
| No sé cuál. | (I don't know which.) |
| Sé muy poco | (I know very little) |
| Y eso sí es mal. | (And this is very bad.) |

Okay, let's say that verse together.

**Narrator:** Make sure you sing along.

**Tony & Lisa:**

|  |  |
|---|---|
| No sé cómo. | (I don't know how.) |
| No sé cuál. | (I don't know which.) |
| Sé muy poco | (I know very little) |
| Y eso sí es mal. | (And this is very bad.) |

**Lisa:** Great. This isn't hard.

**Tony:** No, not at all. Let's sing the whole thing.

**Narrator:** And you can sing along.

**Tony & Lisa:**

|  |  |
|---|---|
| No sé cuándo. | (I don't know when) |
| No sé quién. | (I don't know who) |
| No sé nada | (I don't know anything) |
| Muy bien. | (Very well.) |

|  |  |
|---|---|
| No sé cómo. | (I don't know how.) |
| No sé cuál. | (I don't know which.) |
| Sé muy poco | (I know very little) |
| Y eso sí es mal. | (And this is very bad.) |

**Lisa:** Hmmm. That's strange.

**Tony:** What?

**Lisa:** Well, "mal" means bad, right? Don't you think it's strange that Grandpa's neighbor would be named "Malo"?

**Tony:** You're right, that is strange. Finding what Grandpa hid is more important, though. What should we do now?

**Lisa:** Well, we found "cuándo." It seems like the next word we could look for would be "quién."

**Tony:** Look, over there, through those bushes... Does that tree have writing on it too?

**Lisa:** Let's go check!

**Narrator:** You both clamor through the brush, deeper into the jungle. Sure enough, that tree has "quién" written on it. From that tree, you see a tree marked "nada" even further off. Slowly but surely you begin to move farther and farther away from the house of your grandfather, and you begin to be nervous, remembering your promise to your parents. The precious minutes you have left tick by.

**Lisa:** Okay. There should only be one more tree, the one marked "mal." Do you see it?

**Tony:** There it is! Over there!

**Narrator:** The tree does indeed look "mal." It is dark and twisted. There are no leaves on the branches, and there is a creepy looking hollow in the trunk. You reach into the hollow, and pull out a beat-up old spiral notebook.

**Tony:** Yes!

**Lisa:** We found it!

 **Turn the audio off.**

## PERFORMANCE CHALLENGE:

Now that you have learned a new poem, share your Spanish with a parent, friend, or one of your brothers or sisters by teaching them the poem. Remember to teach it in Spanish and then translate the words into English if your partner does not understand Spanish.

# The Three Pigs I

*(Scatter Chart)*

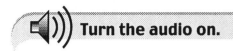 **Turn the audio on.**

*Track 4*

**Narrator:** Monday, 2 p.m.

**Lisa:** What does the notebook say?

**Tony:** It says: "Notes on the De Consuelo Mystery." These must be the notes that Grandpa took when he was looking for clues! This will be very useful. The first thing he wrote was: "The first hint I received from the De Consuelo memoirs took me to the beach outside Progreso. I found that I would need to know a new story in Spanish in order to find the next clue."

**Lisa:** It might take awhile to learn the story. What we need to do now is get to the beach.

**Narrator:** You both run back to the house. As you approach, you see Malo outside of his house gardening again.

**Tony:** Quick, Lisa! Hide the letter and the notebook!

**Malo:** Niños, ha llegado el correo? Dénmelo.

**Lisa:** What is he saying?

**Tony:** I don't know.

**Lisa:** I don't trust him.

**Tony:** Neither do I. Let's go back over to Grandpa's house.

**Narrator:** You go back to the house, and sit on the porch, looking over the notebook.

**Tony:** What should we do?

**Lisa:** We need to learn that story.

**Tony:** Yeah. It looks like Grandpa wrote down some of the words we'll need to know. Let's take a look at them.

*Look at the pictures on your workbook page and choose the picture that fits what you hear.*
*Just point to the picture.*

Track 5

**se escapa**
*escapes*

**la casa de ladrillos**
*the house of bricks*

**mucha hambre**
*very hungry*

**hermano número dos**
*brother number two*

**sale**
*leaves*

**sopla**
*blows*

**hermano número tres**
*brother number three*

**se cae**
*it falls*

**viene**
*comes*

**la madre**
*the mother*

**la casa de leñas**
*the house of sticks*

**el padre**
*the father*

**cochinitos**
*little pigs*

**la casa de paja**
*the house of straw*

**hermano número uno**
*brother number one*

 **Turn the audio off.**

## PERFORMANCE CHALLENGE:

Choose five of the new words and pictures that you learned in the Scatter Chart. Show the pictures to a parent, friend, or one of your brothers or sisters and explain to them how you think the picture represents the words you have learned.

# The Three Pigs I

## (Match and Learn)

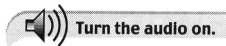 **Turn the audio on.**

5
*Track 6*

**Lisa:** Okay. I think I'm beginning to understand those words.

**Tony:** Me too. Okay. If we're going to find Marcela, we should ask Malo where she is.

**Narrator:** You both go over to the edge of the yard and call to Malo.

**Malo:** ¿Ahora qué quieren?

**Tony:** Um... Señora. Um. Marcela?

**Malo:** Marcela?

**Tony:** Sí, sí, Marcela. Do you know where she is?

**Malo:** Miren, yo no hablo inglés. Salió a pasear. ¿Me entienden? Ella se fue.

**Narrator:** With that, Malo points down the road and goes back inside his own house.

**Lisa:** Oh, no. She must have already left. We're too late.

**Tony:** That's okay. It gives us a little more time. Let's see if we can figure out some more words from that story.

*Practice your new Spanish words and phrases by pointing to the pictures when you hear the words. Look at picture box #1 in your workbook and point to the word or phrase you that hear.*

5
*Track 7*

**1.**

**2.**

**3.**

**4.**

**5.**

**6.**

**7.**

**8.**

**9.**

**10.**

**11.**

**12.**

**13.**

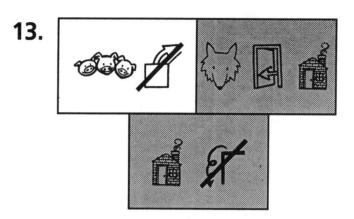

**14.**

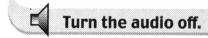

**Turn the audio off.**

## PERFORMANCE CHALLENGE:

Draw a scene using the pictures you learned in your Match and Learn exercise. After you draw your picture, describe each part of the scene to a parent, friend, or one of your brothers or sisters. Remember to use as much Spanish as you can to talk about your drawing.

# The Three Pigs I

*(Diglot Weave)*

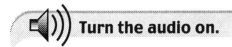 **Turn the audio on.**

Track 8

**Lisa:** Now if we could only find Marcela!

**Tony:** Maybe if we run we can catch her down the road.

**Lisa:** It's worth a try. Come on!

**Narrator:** You both go inside your house and ask your mother if you may go down the street to look for Marcela. Your parents are friends with Marcela from the last trip they made down to Yucatán, and they agree. As quickly as you can, both of you begin running down the road in the direction Malo pointed. A few minutes later you see a very small, dark-haired young lady walking down the road away from you.

**Lisa:** Do you think that's her?

**Tony:** There's only one way to find out.

**Lisa:** Hola! Hola, señorita!

**Narrator:** The young lady turns around. She has a pleasant face and warm eyes. She is very small, not much taller than you. She looks like she is about sixteen years old.

**Marcela:** Hola niños.

**Lisa:** Hola. Me llamo Lisa.

**Tony:** Y yo me llamo Tony.

**Marcela:** Mucho gusto. Me llamo Marcela.

**Lisa:** It's her! It's her! Do you speak English?

**Marcela:** A little.

**Narrator:** You are very happy to meet your cousin. Marcela walks back with you to Grandpa Glen's cottage. You tell her everything that has been happening. With her help, you go through the story that Grandpa left for you to learn.

*I have copied down two versions of "The Three Little Pigs" for you. I felt you might be spooked by so many new words, so I'll first give you a simpler version of the story. Listen.*

Track 9

"Once upon a time there were  .

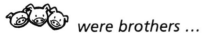 were brothers ...  .

This is their  ; this is their  .

This is el  .

This is el  .

This is el  ...the little brother...el hermanito.

Each of the  builds una  .

Una  for  ...el hermanito,

Una  for  , y

Una  for  .

El  comes.

He comes with much hunger.

He comes to  .

El  ...el hermanito, is in his  .

El  blows.

La  falls: CRASH!

But fortunately el  escapes.

He runs to  .

Now el  comes to  .

 está in his  .

 is also in  .

El  comes with mucha hunger.

El . 

The falls CRASH!

But fortunately los escape.

They run a la .

Now el comes to .

He comes with mucha, mucha hunger.

The are in .

El . Él again.

Él y .

But does not fall.

And so el with mucha, mucha hunger. "

🔊 **Turn the audio off.**

## PERFORMANCE CHALLENGE:

There are four parts to this Performance Challenge:
1. Read the story silently to yourself.
2. Read the story aloud to yourself.
3. Read the story aloud to a parent, friend or one of your brothers and sisters.
4. Retell the story in your own words, using as much Spanish as you can, to a parent, friend or one of your brothers or sisters. Don't worry if you can't remember every word. Do the best you can, and review the audio if you need to.

# The Three Pigs I

*(Review Questions)*

  **Turn the audio on.**

**Narrator:** You are happy to find that Marcela is as worried about your Grandpa as you are.

**Marcela:** ¿Necesitan ayudarle a Glen?

**Tony:** Sí, muchas gracias. We need to go to the beach.

**Marcela:** ¿La playa? Bueno, vamonos.

**Narrator:** After your parents have given their permission, Marcela takes you in her truck to the beach. In the car, you both review with each other what you remember about the story. Be sure to answer!

**Note: Review questions are audio only.**

 **Turn the audio off.**

# The Three Pigs II

*(Scatter Chart)*

 **Turn the audio on.**

*Track 11* **Lisa:** Look at that! This beach is enormous.

**Narrator:** You both explore the beach and the water. The water is warm this near the shore, and you swim until you are covered in salt. There are many interesting things on the beach, including white, chalky pieces of coral that have washed ashore and beautiful stones worn smooth by the water. You walk along the beach for hours.

**Lisa:** I don't know how we're ever going to find anything!

**Tony:** Neither do I. We're running out of time.

**Lisa:** Well, let's take a break and see if we can learn any more of the story. It might help us.

**Tony:** You're right. Here are some new words.

*Track 12* *Look at the pictures and words on your workbook page and choose the picture that fits what you hear. Just point to the picture.*

cuento
*story*

buena idea
*good idea*

llama
*calls out*

noche
*night*

día
*day*

tumbar
*to topple*

pienso
*I think*

hacer
*to make*

**Turn the audio off.**

## PERFORMANCE CHALLENGE:

Choose five of the new words and pictures that you learned in the Scatter Chart. Show the pictures to a parent, friend, or one of your brothers or sisters and explain to them how you think the picture represents the words you have learned.

# The Three Pigs II

## *(Match and Learn)*

 **Turn the audio on.**

**Tony:** Look! What's that down the beach? It looks like an old hut, up on that ridge.

**Narrator:** Marcela and the rest of you scramble up the slight embankment and approach the hut. It is very, very old.

**Lisa:** Should we knock on the door?

**Marcela:** Sí, está bien. He is my friend.

**Narrator:** Marcela knocks. The door is answered by a very old, very small man. He smiles in a friendly way. He and Marcela speak to each other in Spanish for a moment, and she introduces you.

**Miguel:** Hola niños.

**Tony:** Hola, me llamo Tony.

**Miguel:** Mucho gusto en conocerte, Tony. Me llamo Miguel. ¿Te puedo ayudar?

**Tony:** Sí, gracias. ¿Habla usted inglés?

**Miguel:** A little.

**Lisa:** We are trying to help our grandpa, Glen.

**Miguel:** Ah, Glen. He was here about a week ago.

**Tony:** Do you know what he wanted?

**Miguel:** Yes. He was looking for something in my house. You can come in and look if you want.

**Tony:** Thank you.

**Narrator:** Miguel lets you into his tiny hut. There is almost nothing inside, except a hammock, an old stone statue, a bundle of wood, and a straw mat on the floor.

**Tony:** How will we know where to find it?

**Lisa:** It must have something to do with the story. Let's see what we can figure out.

*Practice your new Spanish words and phrases by pointing to the pictures when you hear the words. Look at picture box #1 in your workbook and point to the word or phrase you hear.*

**1.**

**2.**

**3.**

**4.**

**5.**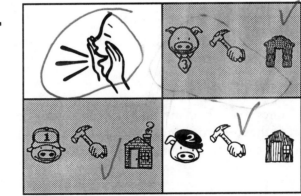

**6.**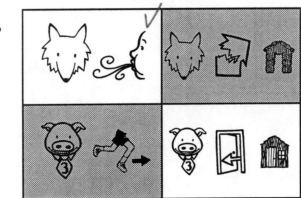

**7.**

**8.**

 **Turn the audio off.**

## PERFORMANCE CHALLENGE:

Draw a scene using the pictures you learned in your Match and Learn exercise. After you draw your picture, describe each part of the scene to a parent, friend, or one of your brothers or sisters. Remember to use as much Spanish as you can to talk about your drawing.

# The Three Pigs II

*(Diglot Weave)*

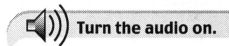 **Turn the audio on.**

*Track 15*

**Lisa:** Mother and Father wanted us home in less than an hour. We'd better hurry. What does Grandpa's book say?

**Tony:** Let me see. It says, "The memoirs indicated that the clue would be hidden in 'la casa que no se cae.'" That sounds familiar. It must be in the story. Let's recheck it one more time.

*Here is the second version I found of "The Three Little Pigs...Los tres cochinitos"*
*Like other cuentos of its kind, it begins with the words Once upon a time. In Spanish we say it this way: Había una vez. Once upon a time...Había una vez.*
*Track 16*

*Now I'll begin el cuento. Había una vez, tres cochinitos. This is su padre; ésta es su madre. Los tres cochinitos were hermanos. Éste es el hermano número uno, el hermano mayor. Éste es el hermano número dos. Y éste es el hermano número tres, el hermanito.*

*Un día el hermano número tres, el hermanito, dice: "I think I'll make me a house...Pienso hacerme una casa. I think I'll make me a house of straw. Pienso hacerme una casa de paja."*

*El hermano mayor says to him: "Oh, little brother, that no es a good idea...Oh, hermanito, eso no es buena idea. Believe me, una casa de paja is no good...no vale."*

*Pero el hermanito doesn't listen to his hermano mayor. In a very short time...en muy poco tiempo, he builds himself una casa de paja. Against the advice of su hermano mayor, este cochinito se construye una casa de paja. He is not very wise, is he? No es muy sabio.*

*El hermano número dos, dice: "I think I'll make me a house, too...Pienso hacerme una casa también. Pienso hacerme una casa de leñas."*

*El hermano mayor le dice: "Oh, hermano, eso no es buena idea. Believe me, una casa de leñas no vale. No vale."*

Pero el cochinito número dos doesn't listen to his hermano mayor. En poco tiempo...he builds himself una casa de leñas. Against the advice of su hermano mayor, este cochinito se construye una casa de leñas. He is not very wise, is he? Like his hermanito, he also no es muy sabio.

El hermano mayor dice: "Yo pienso hacerme una casa también. Pero yo pienso hacerme una casa de ladrillos." El hermano mayor es muy sabio. With great care, he se construye una casa de ladrillos. No de paja, no de leñas, but de ladrillos. Una casa buena.

Then, un día, viene el lobo. He hasn't eaten for dos días, y su estómago is growling. The miserable creature tiene hambre, mucha hambre.

El lobo stops...se para...en frente de la casa de paja. He sniffs. Mmm, there is a delicious cochinito en esta casa. He goes up to la puerta de la casa. El toca a la puerta (knock-knock), y calls out: "Cochinito, cochinito, let me entrar."

El cochinito dice: "No way...ni modo. Tú, you, are the big bad lobo. No te dejo entrar!"

"Well then," dice el lobo, "If you no me dejas entrar, yo voy a soplar y foplar, y voy a tumbar tu casa." Then el lobo sopló y fopló, y tumbó la casa de paja.

Afortunadamente, el cochinito corrió a la casa de su hermano, la casa de leñas.

El lobo chased el cochinito, pero couldn't catch him.

El lobo stops...se para...en frente de la casa de leñas. He knows there is at least one delicious cochinito inside. He goes up to la puerta de la casa. El toca a la puerta (knock-knock), y calls out: "Cochinito, cochinito, let me entrar."

El cochinito dice: "No way, no way...ni modo, ni modo! Tú eres el lobo, el ferocious lobo. No te dejo entrar!" Well then, dice el lobo, "If you no me dejas entrar, yo voy a soplar y foplar, y voy a tumbar tu casa." Then el lobo sopló y fopló, y tumbó la casa de leñas del cochinito número dos.

*Afortunadamente, los dos cochinitos corren a la casa del hermano mayor, la casa de ladrillos.* *El lobo chases after los dos cochinitos, pero can't catch them.*

*Now el lobo se para en frente de la casa de ladrillos. He knows there are at least two delicious cochinitos en la casa. El lobo se acerca a la puerta de la casa...toca a la puerta (knock-knock), y llama: "Cochinito, cochinito, déjame entrar."*

*El cochinito mayor dice: "¡Ni modo, ni modo! Tú eres el lobo, el feroz lobo. No te dejo entrar!"*

*"Bueno pues," dice el lobo,"If no me dejas entrar, yo voy a soplar y foplar. Voy a tumbar tu casa." Then el lobo sopló y fopló...y sopló y fopló, pero he could not tumbar la casa del cochinito mayor, la casa de ladrillos.*

*Pobre, miserable lobo, he had to go home hungry.*

 **Turn the audio off.**

## PERFORMANCE CHALLENGE:

There are four parts to this Performance Challenge:
1. Read the story silently to yourself.
2. Read the story aloud to yourself.
3. Read the story aloud to a parent, friend or one of your brothers and sisters.
4. Retell the story in your own words, using as much Spanish as you can, to a parent, friend or one of your brothers or sisters. Don't worry if you can't remember every word. Do the best you can, and review the audio if you need to.

# The Three Pigs II

*(Story Telling)*

 **Turn the audio on.**

**Lisa:** Okay, so when it says, "la casa que no se cae," it means, "the house that would not fall." And that house is...

**Tony:** The house of stone. Hey! That statue is made of stone!

**Lisa:** You're right! Let's look closer.

**Narrator:** You both go over to the statue. It takes both of you to move it. Underneath is a piece of parchment.

**Lisa:** It looks like another puzzle. This one looks hard. Look, though, it looks like all of the words are from the story, *Los tres cochinitos*. Do you think that we remember enough of it to solve the puzzle?

**Tony:** I think we do. Hey, I have an idea. Let's go through the story and try to tell it ourselves. We can help each other.

**Lisa:** That's a great idea! We can look at the pictures to help us.

*Now retell the story in your own words, using as much Spanish as possible.*

 **Turn the audio off.**

# Word Puzzle 1

## (The Three Pigs)

🔊 **Turn the audio on.**

**Tony:** Okay. Let's see if the puzzle makes any sense.

🔊 **Turn the audio off.**

*Fill in the blanks in the puzzle below by following the numbered clues. The letters that fall in the circled blanks will make an additional word that will help you on your adventure.*

 1. *mother*

2. **Brothers**

3. **Bricks**

4. **They run**
*corrio*

5.  *house*

6. *father*

7. **Boy**

1. madra
2. hermanas
3. indrillos
4. carnia
5. casa
6. padra
7.

**Turn the audio on.**

**Tony:** "Mercado." What does that mean?

**Lisa:** Oh no! We have to get back home! It's past time for us to go!

**Tony:** Thank you, Miguel.

**Lisa:** Yeah, thanks.

**Miguel:** You're welcome. Good luck.

**Turn the audio off.**

# A Circus Act

*(Horseshoe Story)*

  **Turn the audio on.**

**Narrator:** Tuesday, 10 a.m. Marcela understood the clue "mercado" to mean the market at Mérida, the capital city of Yucatán, and your parents have agreed to let you go with her today.

**Lisa:** Could this really be the right place? There are so many people here.

**Tony:** We're never going to be able to find anything in this crowd. What does Grandpa say in his notebook about where to find the next clue?

**Lisa:** Let me see. "The map I found led me to the 'mercado' in Mérida." Oh, good! We're in the right place. "The next clue in the memoirs said that I must 'buscar al elefante.' I understood it to refer to the story of *A Circus Act.*" Here, he tells the story.

 *Listen to this story and read as you listen. You will learn to recite this story in Spanish using pictures to help you remember the words.*

## A Circus Act

*En el circo hay un elefante, he aquí el elefante.*

*Un tigre salta sobre la espalda del elefante.*

*Un perro salta sobre la espalda del tigre.*

*Un mono salta sobre la espalda del perro.*

*Un gato salta sobre la espalda del mono.*

*De repente un ratón pasa corriendo.*

*El gato salta de la espalda del mono.*

*El mono salta de la espalda del perro.*

*El perro salta de la espalda del tigre.*

*El tigre salta de la espalda del elefante.*

*El elefante, el tigre, el perro, el mono, y el gato persiguen al ratón.*

*Pero el ratón se escapa.*

*¡Que suerte tuvo el ratón!*

 **Turn the audio off.**

### PERFORMANCE CHALLENGE:

Create hand actions to represent the actions in the horseshoe story. (For example: Make up different actions to represent the animals you heard about in the story.) After you have created the actions, perform your mini-play for a parent, friend, or one of your bothers and sisters. Remember to narrate your actions in Spanish and then translate your words if your audience does not understand Spanish.

# A Circus Act

## (Match and Learn)

 **Turn the audio on.**

*Track 22*

**Tony:** "Elefante." That sounds like "elephant," doesn't it?

**Lisa:** Yeah, you're right. We should go look for an elephant.

**Tony:** Well, that could be anything. It could be a statue, or a painting, or, or in a zoo, or...

**Lisa:** Hey...look! Isn't that Grandpa Glen's neighbor? The one with the bad name...Malo?

**Tony:** You're right! What is he doing here?

**Marcela:** Oh, Malo. Él no me cae bien. I don't like him.

**Lisa:** I know. I don't want him to see us.

**Narrator:** Quickly all of you duck into an alley behind a booth.

**Tony:** Is he gone?

**Lisa:** No, he's still wandering around out there. It looks like he's searching for someone.

**Tony:** I don't trust him. Hey, look at that! On the wall! There's a mural of an elephant!

**Lisa:** You're right! It's a good thing we hid in here, otherwise we would have never found it.

**Tony:** Well, look. A little farther down the mural is a picture of a tiger. Was there a tiger in the story? Let's look through the words we need to know for the story and check.

*Look at picture box #1 in your workbook.*

*Track 23*

**1.**

**2.**
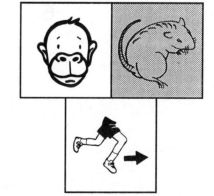

**3.**

**4.**

**5.**

**6.**

**Tony:** Well, that's it, then. Let's follow the animals back and see where they take us.

**Lisa:** But, Tony, it's almost 3 p.m. We have to go back home soon.

**Tony:** I don't wanna go out there again. We might run into Malo. Come on, we'll be quick.

**Narrator:** You begin to follow the trail of animals through the streets of Mérida.

 **Turn the audio off.**

## PERFORMANCE CHALLENGE:

Draw a scene using the pictures you learned in your Match and Learn exercise. After you draw your picture, describe each part of the scene to a parent, friend, or one of your brothers or sisters. Remember to use as much Spanish as you can to talk about your drawing.

# A Circus Act

*(Horseshoe Story Review)*

 **Turn the audio on.**

**Narrator:** Tuesday, 3 p.m. You stand in front of a beautiful old mansion. You have followed the trail of animals here.

**Lisa:** What is this place?

**Tony:** The sign says it's called the Casa de Montejo. This must be the place. It's one of the oldest houses in Yucatán. We should go look around.

**Lisa:** Look! There! There's a mouse painted on the wall there!

**Narrator:** You all crowd close to look. There is a mouse, and underneath it, in a crack in the wall, you find another puzzle folded up.

**Lisa:** It looks like it uses words from *The Circus Act*. We should review the story and make sure we know it well enough to do the puzzle.

*Listen to this story and read as you listen. You will learn to recite this story in Spanish using pictures to help you remember the words.*

## A Circus Act

*En el circo hay un elefante, he aquí el elefante.*

*Un tigre salta sobre la espalda del elefante.*

*Un perro salta sobre la espalda del tigre.*

*Un mono salta sobre la espalda del perro.*

*Un gato salta sobre la espalda del mono.*

*De repente un ratón pasa corriendo.*

*El gato salta de la espalda del mono.*

*El mono salta de la espalda del perro.*

*El perro salta de la espalda del tigre.*

*El tigre salta de la espalda del elefante.*

*El elefante, el tigre, el perro, el mono, y el gato persiguen al ratón.*

*Pero el ratón se escapa.*

*¡Que suerte tuvo el ratón!*

 **Turn the audio off.**

## PERFORMANCE CHALLENGE:

Create hand actions to represent the actions in the horseshoe story. (For example: Make up different actions to represent the animals you heard about in the story.) After you have created the actions, perform your mini-play for a parent, friend, or one of your bothers and sisters. Remember to narrate your actions in Spanish and then translate your words if your audience does not understand Spanish.

# Word Puzzle 2

## (A Circus Act)

Track 27

🔊)) **Turn the audio on.**

**Tony:** Okay, I think I know the story perfectly. Let's see if we can do the puzzle now.

🔊 **Turn the audio off.**

*Fill in the blanks in the puzzle below by following the numbered clues. The letters that fall in the circled blanks will make additional words that will help you on your adventure.*

**1.**

**2.**

**3.**

**4. He jumps**

**5.**

**6.**

**7. He escapes**   **8.**

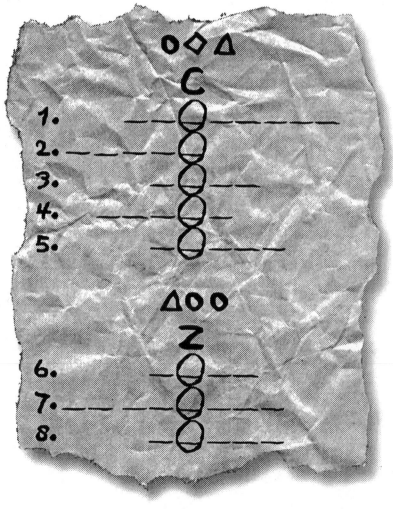

 **Turn the audio on.**

*Track 28* **Lisa:** "Cenote Zaci." What is that?

**Marcela:** Está cerca de mi casa. It is near Valladolid.

**Tony:** Isn't that where you live? Hey... that reminds me! We have to go! We're gonna be home late !

**Turn the audio off.**

# Test 1

## (Review)

 **Turn the audio on.**

*Track 29*

**Narrator:** As you drive home in the darkening evening, you look over Marcela's map of Yucatán.

**Lisa:** I found it! It's over here, next to Valladolid. It's far away! Marcela, could you take us there?

**Marcela:** Sí. I need to go home soon anyway.

**Tony:** Do you think Mom and Dad will let us go? It's pretty far away. And we're already going to be home a little late tonight!

**Lisa:** Yes, but think how much Spanish we have learned!

**Tony:** Hey! That's a good idea! Maybe if we could show our parents how much Spanish we've learned, they would let us go to Zaci.

**Lisa:** That's worth a try! We'd better practice before we get home.

## A. Frame Identifications

*For each question, you will see a box with pictures. You will hear a statement about one of the pictures. There will be a pause of 10 seconds to identify the picture, and then the statement will be repeated.*

*Track 30*

**1.**

**2.**

**3.**

**4.**

**5.**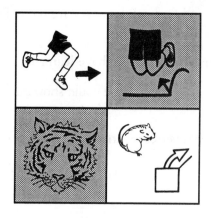

## Comprehension Multiple-Choice

*Complete the following conversations by choosing the correct answer from the options listed.*

1. ¿Cómo está usted?"

    A. ¡Hasta luego!

    B. Muy bien, gracias.

    C. Chao pues.

    D. Me alegro verte hoy.

2. The little pig built his house out of paja. ¿Eso es buena idea?"

    A. Sí, eso toca a la puerta.

    B. Sí, es muy sabio.

    C. No, no es muy sabio.

    D. No, no me dejas entrar.

3. Who built his house out of paja?

    A. El tigre

    B. El perro

C. El cochinito número tres, el hermanito

D. la zorra

4. Who gets away from the circus act?

A. El ratón.

B. El gato.

C. El elefante.

D. El mono.

5. How would Tony introduce himself in Spanish?

A. No sé nada Tony.

B. Me alegro verte hoy Tony.

C. Me llamo Tony.

D. Sé muy poco Tony.

*Now go on to complete the reading/writing portion of this test.*

## Turn the audio off.

Matching

*Choose the statements that match and draw a line to connect the two.*

1. wolf                       A. casa

2. straw                      B. cochinito

3. house                      C. la casa de ladrillos

4. house of bricks            D. lobo

5. little pig                 E. paja

True or False

*Write T or F for each statement.*

_____ 1. El hermanito built his casa out of paja.

_____ 2. El cochinito número tres built his casa out of leñas.

_____ 3. El lobo entra en la casa de ladrillos.

_____ 4. El cochinito número dos se cae on his hermano.

_____ 5. El cochinito número uno se escapa from el lobo.

# Answer Key

**1.**

**2.**

**3.**

**4.**

**5.**

**Comprehension Multiple-Choice**

1. B. Muy bien, gracias.

2. C. No, no es muy sabio.

3. C. El cochinito número tres, el hermanito

4. A. El ratón.

5. C. Me llamo Tony.

**Matching**

1. D

2. E

3. A

4. C

5. B

**True or False**

1. T

2. F

3. F

4. F

5. T

# The Adventure Continues

*(The Adventure Continues)*

 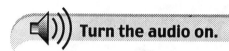

Track 1

**Narrator:** Wednesday, 10 a.m. Having impressed your parents with how much Spanish you have learned, they agree to let Marcela take you back with her to Zaci. You had to leave early in the morning, when the sun was just coming up and the sky was still gray, in order to arrive in Zaci before 10 a.m. Marcela is going to her house in Valladolid and left a phone number for you to call her.

**Lisa:** Look, here. There's a sign about Zaci. "Cenote Zaci are a system of caves worn through the limestone rock by underground rivers."

**Tony:** Underground rivers? I've never even heard of such a thing before. How is that possible?

**Lisa:** I don't know. It sounds cool, though. Let's go inside.

**Narrator:** You have never seen anything like these caves before in your life. In order to get inside, you must climb down thin steps carved into the stone side of the cave. Inside, the light reflects off of the blue pools of water and the grayish white of the limestone. There are many offshoots in the caves, that travel in many directions.

**Lisa:** Look at that. The sign said that these caves can wander off for miles.

**Tony:** How will we ever find the clue in all of this? It must be huge. I'll bet there's parts that no one has ever even set foot in.

**Lisa:** I think it's beautiful. Still, it's kind of scary at the same time, isn't it?

**Tony:** Yeah. I can just imagine that pirate, what's his name, De Consuelo, running around down here.

**Narrator:** You begin to search the caves. You wander around for hours, being very careful to remember where you turn. Getting lost in these caves would be a very bad idea. You wonder if you will ever be able to find the clue.

**Lisa:** Well, I'm almost ready to give up. Let's go and call Marcela.

**Tony:** The paper she left us says, "42.68.79."

**Lisa:** That doesn't sound like a phone number.

**Tony:** I know. Maybe phone numbers are different in Mexico. Should we try calling it?

**Lisa:** Yeah. There was a phone booth a little bit down the road. Do you have any money?

**Tony:** A few pesos. It should be enough.

**Lisa:** I hope so. Come on.

**Narrator:** You leave the cave.

**Tony:** What time is it?

**Lisa:** Um...it's about 1 p.m.

**Tony:** Why is it so dark outside, then?

**Lisa:** I don't know. That's kind of strange.

**Narrator:** Just then, there is a deafening thunderclap, and a downpour begins. You both run as fast as you can to the phone booth but are soaked through by the time you get there.

 **Turn the audio off.**

## PERFORMANCE CHALLENGE:

Now that you have read about different places in Yucatán, locate some pictures of the area. Try looking in an encyclopedia or online to see what Yucatán really looks like!

# Uno, dos, tres niñitos

## *(Ditties)*

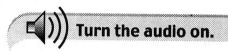

Track 2

**Narrator:** Wednesday, 1 p.m. You both cram into the phone booth. You are wet and shivering.

**Lisa:** I've never seen a storm blow up so quickly before.

**Tony:** Neither have I. It's kind of creepy.

**Lisa:** Yeah. Could it be a hurricane? Do they have hurricanes here?

**Tony:** Well, if they do, I bet they look just like this.

**Lisa:** Do you still have your pesos? We should try to call Marcela.

**Tony:** Yeah. Here. Now, what was the number?

**Lisa:** Okay, it was 42...

**Tony:** Hold on. Wait a minute. I can't get the numbers on the phone to work. Oh, I think they might be broken. They won't push in or anything.

**Lisa:** Well, what now?

**Operator:** ¿Te puedo ayudar?

**Tony:** It's the operator. Um... habla inglés?

**Operator:** No, lo siento. No hablo inglés.

**Tony:** Oh. Muchas gracias.

**Lisa:** Great. What now?

**Tony:** Its scary, trying to speak Spanish to someone that doesn't know any English.

**Lisa:** Yeah. Couldn't we just tell her the number in Spanish?

**Tony:** You're right. It can't be that hard. It's just numbers, right?

**Lisa:** Right. Do you remember the song that Grandpa taught us? "Uno, Dos, Tres Niñitos"?

**Tony:** Yeah. How did it go again?

**Lisa:** Listen.

| | |
|---|---|
| Uno, dos, tres niñitos | *(One, two, three little children)* |
| Cuatro, cinco, seis niñitos | *(Four, five, six little children)* |
| Siete, ocho, nueve niñitos | *(Seven, eight, nine little children)* |
| Diez niñitos buenos. | *(Ten good little children)* |

Let's sing it again together.

**Narrator:** Be sure to sing along.

**Tony & Lisa:**

| | |
|---|---|
| Uno, dos, tres niñitos | *(One, two, three little children)* |
| Cuatro, cinco, seis niñitos | *(Four, five, six little children)* |
| Siete, ocho, nueve niñitos | *(Seven, eight, nine little children)* |
| Diez niñitos buenos. | *(Ten good little children)* |

**Tony:** Okay. That's easy. Let's try one more time.

**Narrator:** Go ahead sing along.

**Tony & Lisa:**

| | |
|---|---|
| Uno, dos, tres niñitos | *(One, two, three little children)* |
| Cuatro, cinco, seis niñitos | *(Four, five, six little children)* |
| Siete, ocho, nueve niñitos | *(Seven, eight, nine little children)* |
| Diez niñitos buenos. | *(Ten good little children)* |

**Lisa:** Okay. Think you can do it?

**Tony:** Sure. Why not?

**Operator:** ¿Te puedo ayudar?

**Narrator:** See if you can say the numbers in Spanish. (42.68.79)

**Operator:** un momento...

**Tony:** We did it! She's going to connect us!

 **Turn the audio off.**

## PERFORMANCE CHALLENGE:

Now that you have learned a new song, share your Spanish with a parent, friend, or one of your brothers or sisters by teaching them the song. Remember to teach it in Spanish and then translate the words into English if your partner does not understand Spanish.

Back at Marcela's house, Tony and Lisa changed into some dry clothes and then drank some hot chocolate to help them get warm. Try the recipe below and find out what Mexican hot chocolate really tastes like. Remember to ask your parents for help making this recipe.

## Mexican Hot Chocolate

4 cups milk

3/4 tsp ground cinnamon

3 oz. unsweetened chocolate, chopped fine

1/3 cup firmly packed light brown sugar

1 1/2 tsp vanilla

cinnamon sticks

In a saucepan, combine the milk, the brown sugar, the cinnamon, the vanilla, and bring the mixture to a boil over moderate heat. In a small bowl, combine the chocolate with 1/2 cup of the hot milk mixture and whisk until the chocolate is melted and the mixture is smooth. Add the chocolate mixture to the remaining milk mixture and simmer the hot chocolate, whisking, for two minutes. Divide the hot chocolate among mugs and serve it with cinnamon sticks as stirrers.

# Abuelito

## *(Ditties)*

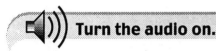 **Turn the audio on.**

Track 3

**Narrator:** Wednesday, 4:30 p.m. Marcela has picked you up and taken you to her parents house, which is not very far from the caves. You greet her parents, who are impressed with how much Spanish you know. To your extreme disappointment, however, the storm outside has just gotten stronger and stronger. It has made it impossible to go back to Zaci. Fortunately, it has also made it impossible to drive home, and so you will have another day to explore the caves. Marcela called your parents and got permission. Then went out to buy some groceries for dinner.

**Lisa:** This is terrible. How are we ever supposed to get anything done if we can't even get back to the caves?

**Tony:** Do you know what else is bothering me?

**Lisa:** What?

**Tony:** I'm sure that Malo, the neighbor, is the person that Grandpa Glen was talking about when he said someone was trying to sabotage him.

**Lisa:** It's possible.

**Tony:** It's very possible. So, if he is the one, Mom and Dad might tell him that we're spending the night in Zaci. He might try to come and stop us.

**Lisa:** That's kind of scary. I wish we could get back to the caves. Is there anything in the notebook?

**Tony:** Let me check. Yeah, look at this. It just looks like scribbles, though.

**Lisa:** What if it's a map of the caves? Look, if that big circle there is the entrance...

**Tony:** Yeah... I think you may be right! Is there anything that might mark where the clue would be?

**Lisa:** Well, there's notes over the whole thing. Look, where it says, "manantial," and there "aquí," and here "quebradura en la pared." How should we know where to look?

**Tony:** Well, across the top, he wrote, "¿Dónde?" I've heard that word before.

**Lisa:** Yeah, I think I have to. Doesn't that ask where something is? Like in that song that Grandpa taught us?

**Tony:** Which one?

**Lisa:** "Abuelito." Do you remember? It went like this.

| | |
|---|---|
| Abuelito, Abuelito, | *(Grandpa, Grandpa,)* |
| Dónde estás tú? | *(Where are you?)* |
| Dónde estás tú? | *(Where are you?)* |
| Aquí estoy, mi nieto, | *(Here I am, my grandson)* |

| | |
|---|---|
| Aquí estoy, mi nieta, | *(Here I am, my granddaughter)* |
| Yo estoy bien. | *(I am fine.)* |
| Yo estoy bien. | *(I am fine.)* |

**Tony:** Okay. That's not a very hard song. Let's sing it.

**Narrator:** Be sure to sing along.

**Tony & Lisa:**

| | |
|---|---|
| Abuelito, Abuelito, | *(Grandpa, Grandpa,)* |
| Dónde estás tú? | *(Where are you?)* |
| Dónde estás tú? | *(Where are you?)* |
| Aquí estoy, mi nieto, | *(Here I am, my grandson)* |
| Aquí estoy, mi nieta, | *(Here I am, my granddaughter)* |
| Yo estoy bien. | *(I am fine.)* |
| Yo estoy bien. | *(I am fine.)* |

**Lisa:** Good. Once more.

**Tony & Lisa:**

| | |
|---|---|
| Abuelito, Abuelito, | *(Grandpa, Grandpa,)* |
| Dónde estás tú? | *(Where are you?)* |
| Dónde estás tú? | *(Where are you?)* |
| Aquí estoy, mi nieto, | *(Here I am, my grandson)* |
| Aquí estoy, mi nieta, | *(Here I am, my granddaughter)* |
| Yo estoy bien. | *(I am fine.)* |
| Yo estoy bien. | *(I am fine.)* |

**Tony:** Hey, doesn't that song have the word "aquí" in it, like on the map?

**Lisa:** Yeah, you're right. Let's see…"aquí" means "here." That must be where the clue is!

**Tony:** Well, now all we need to do is go back and get it!

 **Turn the audio off.**

### PERFORMANCE CHALLENGE:

Now that you have learned a new song, share your Spanish with a parent, friend, or one of your brothers or sisters by teaching them the song. Remember to teach it in Spanish and then translate the words into English if your partner does not understand Spanish.

# Chicken Little I

## *(Scatter Chart)*

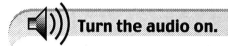 

Track 4

**Narrator:** Wednesday, 5 p.m. Outside, the storm seems finally to be relenting. The sky is still dark and foreboding, but the rain has slackened to a drizzle.

**Lisa:** Are you thinking what I'm thinking? We aren't very far away from the caves. We could go back.

**Tony:** Tonight? We'd have to wait for Marcela. I don't know. It sounds like a bad idea. What if something happened? It's still really dark out there.

**Lisa:** Come on. If we wait until tomorrow to find that clue, then we might never get to Grandpa Glen in time!

**Tony:** You're right. Let's check the notebook, though, until Marcela comes home. We can see if there's anything more we need to learn first.

**Lisa:** Good idea.

**Tony:** Okay, It says, "In order to figure out the next clue, I had to learn a new story in Spanish, called *El Pollito*. Oh, this might be hard. It has a lot of new words in it.

**Lisa:** That's okay. Let's go through them until Marcela gets back.

Track 5

*Look at the pictures on your workbook page and choose the picture that fits what you hear.*

**la cueva**
*the cave*

**la cabeza**
*the head*

**el ganso**
*the goose*

**los ojos**
*the eyes*

**un pedazo**
*a piece*

**el pavo**
*the turkey*

**el cielo**
*the sky*

**la zorra**
*the fox*

**la gallina**
*the hen*

**los animales**
*the animals*

**la hoja**
*the leaf*

**el pollito**
*the chickie*

**el pato**
*the duck*

 **Turn the audio off.**

## PERFORMANCE CHALLENGE:

Choose five of the new words and pictures that you learned in the Scatter Chart. Show the pictures to a parent, friend, or one of your brothers or sisters and explain to them how you think the picture represents the words you have learned.

# Chicken Little I

## *(Match and Learn)*

 **Turn the audio on.**

Track 6

**Narrator:** You don't have to wait long for Marcela to return. She is skeptical about going back to the caves in the storm but finally agrees. Trembling with excitement, you take a flashlight and head out the door. Once outside, you run through the rain over to Marcela's truck. It doesn't take very long, but your shoes and ankles are covered with mud by the time you get there. It only takes a few minutes to arrive at the cave. You all sit in the truck.

**Lisa:** It's even scarier here in the dark.

**Tony:** Too late to turn back now.

**Narrator:** Finally, Marcela convinces you all to make a run through the rain into the cave. You turn on the flashlight and creep down the narrow stone steps back into the cave.

**Tony:** Okay. According to Grandpa Glen's map, we need to take the first right and then two lefts. Okay?

**Lisa:** Okay.

**Narrator:** You all sneak quietly through the caves, following the directions on the map. Finally, you find a small alcove that you missed before.

**Lisa:** "Aquí." This must be it.

**Tony:** It looks kind of scary. What if there are bats or snakes or something inside?

**Lisa:** There's nothing inside except a clue. Do you think we know the story well enough to figure it out?

**Tony:** I don't know. There are still some new words to learn.

**Lisa:** Well, let's go through them, then.

*Picture box #1.*

Track 7

**1.**

**2.**

**3.**    **4.**

**5.**

**6.**

**7.**

**8.**

 **Turn the audio off.**

## PERFORMANCE CHALLENGE:

Draw a scene using the pictures you learned in your Match and Learn exercise. After you draw your picture, describe each part of the scene to a parent, friend, or one of your brothers or sisters. Remember to use as much Spanish as you can to talk about your drawing.

# Chicken Little I

## *(Diglot Weave)*

 **Turn the audio on.**

**Narrator:** You all squeeze into the alcove and begin to look for the clue.

**Tony:** Hey. What's this?

**Lisa:** It looks like a note. It has writing on it. It says, "El cielo se cae."

**Tony:** What does that mean? Marcela, do you know what that means?

**Marcela:** I don't know how you say in English.

**Tony:** That's okay. Isn't it in the story?

**Lisa:** Maybe. Let's go through the story and see if we can figure out what it means.

*"The Sky is Falling." This is the first version of this story that I found. Don't worry about understanding all of the words the first time. Just concentrate on what you know!*

This is the story of a pollito that convinced itself that el cielo was falling. One day this pollito was in the garden when una hoja, a big hoja, fell on her cabeza.

The poor pollito was startled and imagined that el cielo was falling. It started to run, screaming: "Peep, peep,

Mommy, where are you, Mommy?"

"Cluck, cluck, here I am, Pollito. What is it?"

"El cielo is falling! El cielo is falling!"

"How do you know, Pollito?"

"I saw it with my very ojos and un pedazo of it fell on my cabeza. I tell you the truth."

"Let's flee!" screamed la gallina. "Let's flee, run! Pato, Pato, where are you, Pato?"

"Quack, quack, here I am. What happened, what happened?"

"El cielo is falling! El cielo is falling!"

"How do you know, Gallina?"

"Pollito told me."

"How do you know, Pollito?"

*"I saw it with my very ojos, and un pedazo of it fell on my cabeza. I tell you the truth."*

*"Well, let's flee!" screamed Pato. "Let's flee, run! Ganso, Ganso, where are you, Ganso?"*

*"Honk, honk, here I am, Pato. What happened?"*

*"El cielo is falling! El cielo is falling!"*

*"How do you know, Pato?"*

*"Gallina told me."*

*"How do you know, Gallina?"*

*"Pollito told me."*

*"How do you know, Pollito?"*

*"I saw it with my very eyes, and un pedazo of it fell on my cabeza. I tell you the truth."*

*"Oh, let's flee!" screamed Ganso. "Let's flee, run! Pavo, Pavo, where are you, Pavo?"*

*"Gobble, gobble, here I am, Ganso. What happened?"*

*"El cielo is falling! El cielo is falling!"*

*"How do you know, Ganso?"*

*"Pato told me."*

*"How do you know, Pato?"*

*"Gallina told me."*

*"How do you know, Gallina?"*

*"Pollito told me."*

*"How do you know, Pollito?"*

*"Oh, I saw it with my very ojos, and un pedazo of it fell on my cabeza. I tell you the truth."*

*"Well, let's flee!" screamed Pavo. "Let's flee, run! Zorra, Zorra, where are you, Zorra?"*

*"Yif, yif. Here I am. What happened?"*

*"El cielo is falling! El cielo is falling!"*

*"How do you know, Pavo?"*

*"Ganso told me."*

*"How do you know, Ganso?"*

*"Pato told me."*

*"How do you know, Pato?"*

*"Gallina told me."*

*"How do you know, Gallina?"*

*"Pollito told me."*

*"How do you know, Pollito?"*

*"I saw it with my very ojos, and un pedazo of it fell on my cabeza. I tell you the truth."*

*Zorra thought a little and said: "Don't be afraid. I'll save you. Come with me to my cueva."*

*And all the animales went with the Zorra into her cueva. But el pavo y el ganso y el pato y la gallina y el pollito never came out. La zorra ate them all.*

*You see, a false rumor can lead to tragedy.*

 **Turn the audio off.**

## PERFORMANCE CHALLENGE:

There are four parts to this Performance Challenge:
1. Read the story silently to yourself.
2. Read the story aloud to yourself.
3. Read the story aloud to a parent, friend or one of your brothers and sisters.
4. Retell the story in your own words, using as much Spanish as you can, to a parent, friend or one of your brothers or sisters. Don't worry if you can't remember every word. Do the best you can, and review the audio if you need to.

# Chicken Little I

*(Review Questions)*

Track 10

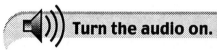 **Turn the audio on.**

**Tony:** What do we need to look for?

**Narrator:** Just then, the batteries in the flashlight give out and you are plunged into darkness.

**Marcela:** ¡Cálmense! It's okay. Stay here, I will go and get another flashlight from my truck.

**Narrator:** Marcela leaves, and you both sit trembling in the dark.

**Lisa:** What are we going to do until she gets back? Tony, I'm scared.

**Tony:** I know, I am too. Let's keep talking. I know, we can review what we know about the story. Marcela will come back soon, I promise.

**Lisa:** Yeah, you're right. Okay. Let's ask each other some questions about the story. Do you think you remember it enough?

**Note: Review questions are audio only.**

 **Turn the audio off.**

# Chicken Little II

*(Scatter Chart)*

**Turn the audio on.**

*Track 11*

**Narrator:** Wednesday, 6 p.m. You sit in the dark cave, frightened.

**Tony:** Shhh. I hear something.

**Malo:** ¿Oí algo? Está alguien allí?

**Lisa:** Doesn't that sound like Grandpa's neighbor, Malo?

**Tony:** Shh!

**Malo:** Espero que no están aquí esos chicos. Han estado arruinando mis planes.

**Tony:** Do you believe me now? Why else would he be here if he isn't trying to stop us from helping Grandpa Glen?

**Malo:** Creo que no están aquí. Mejor me voy.

**Lisa:** Is he gone?

**Tony:** I'm not sure. Let's wait a minute.

**Lisa:** I think he's gone.

**Tony:** It feels like we've been in this cave forever. We'll never know that story well enough to solve the clue.

**Lisa:** Sure we will. We're understanding it more and more each time we go over it. There's just a few more words to understand before we get it all.

*Practice your new Spanish words and phrases by pointing when you hear the words.*

*Track 12*

| | | | |
|---|---|---|---|
| **me lo dijo** *he (she) told me* | **¿cómo lo sabes?** *how do you know it?* | **aquí estoy** *here I am* | **vengan conmigo** *you all come with me* |
| **se está cayendo** *it is falling* | **¿dónde estás?** *where are you?* | **le digo la verdad** *I am telling you the truth* | **lo vi** *I saw it* |

 **Turn the audio off.**

## PERFORMANCE CHALLENGE:

Choose several of the words and phrases that you learned in the Scatter Chart. Write as many sentences as you can using these words and phrases (and others that you already know). If you want to, create your own story with the sentences. Read the sentences that you create to a parent, friend, or one of your brothers or sisters. Remember to translate the Spanish if your partner does not understand Spanish.

# Chicken Little II
## (Match and Learn)

 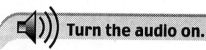

**Narrator:** In the caves, 6:30 p.m. You hear footsteps.

**Tony:** Shh! Malo might be coming back.

**Marcela:** ¡Niños! ¿Están ustedes aquí?

**Lisa:** It's Marcela! Marcela! Marcela, we're over here!

**Narrator:** Marcela brings a flashlight, and takes you back to her house. In no time she and her parents have you tucked into bed.

**Lisa:** Tony? Do you think we'll be able to find Grandpa Glen tomorrow?

**Tony:** I hope so. We need to go back and find that clue, and we'll just have to go from there.

**Lisa:** I don't think I'll be able to sleep. I'm too scared. I can't believe that Malo followed us here.

**Tony:** I know. It frightens me too. I'm also scared that I won't know enough Spanish to figure out the last clues.

**Lisa:** Yeah. Me too.

**Tony:** I've got an idea. Let's go over the last few things we need to know in this story, *El Pollito*.

**Lisa:** What a good idea! I'm not tired yet, anyway.

*Look at picture box #1 in your workbook.*

**1.**

| Where are you? | here I am |
|---|---|
| I saw it | it is falling |

**2.**

| Where are you, Hen? | I saw it |
|---|---|
| the sky is falling | Here I am, Chickie |

**3.**

| How do you know it? | the chickie told it to me |
|---|---|
| I am telling you the truth | you all come with me |

**4.**

| the animals run | Where are you, Goose? |
|---|---|
| Here I am, Hen | the sky is falling |

**5.**

| How do you know it, Hen? | I saw it |
|---|---|
| the chickie told it to me | How do you know it, Chickie? |

**6.**

| I am telling you the truth | you all come with me |
|---|---|
| | the animals run |

**7.**

| hen told it to me | How do you know it, Hen? |
|---|---|
| the sky is falling | How do you know it, Goose? |

**8.**

| you all come with me | the animals and the cave |
|---|---|
| | the animals run |

 **Turn the audio off.**

## PERFORMANCE CHALLENGE:

List all the names of the animals from this activity in **Spanish** and **English** and teach them to a parent, friend, or one of your brothers or sisters.

# Chicken Little II

### (Diglot Weave)

 **Turn the audio on.**

Track 15 **Narrator:** Thursday, 9 a.m. You could hardly wait for Marcela to wake up before you were begging her to let you go back to the caves. She agrees, and lets you walk back to the caves. Once again you find the alcove from the night before.

**Tony:** Okay. Now, the clue says, "El cielo se cae." That's in the story, but we need to figure out what it means.

**Lisa:** Yeah. Let's go through the story one more time.

*Here now is the second version of the story of "Chicken Little." It's a little more advanced, but I think you can follow it. We'll title this story:*

Track 16

"¡El cielo se está  ! ¡El cielo se está 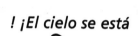 !"

This is the  of a little 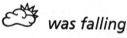 that convinced itself that 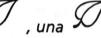 was falling.

One day...Un día this  was in the garden when una , una

grande, fell on her  . The poor was startled and imagined that

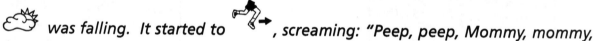 was falling. It started to , screaming: "Peep, peep, Mommy, mommy,

where are you? Mamita, mamita, ¿dónde estás?"

"Cluck, cluck, here I am, 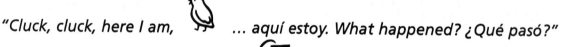 ... aquí estoy. What happened? ¿Qué pasó?"

" is falling! ...¡ se está !"

"How do you know, 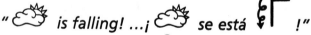 ¿Cómo lo sabes?"

"I saw it with my very , mamita ... I saw it con mis propios . Un

 of sky fell on my . I tell you the truth."

"Let's flee!" screamed . "Let's flee. Run! Duck, Duck, where are you ...

¿dónde estás, ?"

"Quack, quack, here I am ... Aquí estoy. ¿Qué pasó?"

"[sky] se está [falling]! [sky] se está [falling]!"

"Huh? How do you know, [chicken] ... ¿Cómo lo sabes?"

"[chick] told me so...Pollito me lo dijo."

"¿Cómo lo sabes, [chick]?"

"I saw it con mis propios [eyes] [eyes]. Un [piece] de [sky] se [fell] on my [head]. I tell

you the truth ... Le digo la verdad."

"Let's flee! Run!" [clap] [duck]. "¡Huyamos! Run! Goose, Goose, ¿dónde estás,

[goose]?"

"Honk, honk, aquí estoy, [duck]. ¿Qué pasó, qué pasó?"

"¡[sky] se está [falling]! ¡[sky] se está [falling]!"

"Huh, ¿cómo lo sabes, [duck]?"

"[chicken] told me so ... [chicken] me lo dijo."

"¿Cómo lo sabes, [chicken]?"

"[chick] me lo dijo."

"¿Cómo lo sabes, [chick]?"

"I saw it con mis propios [eyes]. Un [piece] de [sky] se me [fell] en [head]. I tell

you the truth ... Le digo la verdad."

"Let's flee!" gritó el [goose]. "¡Corramos! Turkey, Turkey, ¿dónde estás, [turkey]?"

"Gobble, gobble, aquí estoy, [goose]. ¿Qué pasó?"

"¡[sky] se está [falling]! ¡[sky] se está [falling]!"

"Huh, ¿Cómo lo sabes,  ?"

" me lo dijo."

"¿Cómo lo sabes, ?"

" me lo dijo."

"¿Cómo lo sabes, ?"

" me lo dijo."

"¿Cómo lo sabes, ?"

"I saw it ... lo vi con mis propios . Un de se me en la Le digo la verdad."

"¡ !" gritó el . "¡ ! Fox, Fox, where are you, ?"

"Yif, yif. Aquí estoy. ¿Qué pasó?"

" se está ! ¡ se está !"

"Ohhh. ¿Cómo lo sabes, ?"

" me lo dijo."

"¿Cómo lo sabes, ?"

" me lo dijo."

"¿Cómo lo sabes, ?"

" me lo dijo."

"¿Cómo lo sabes, ?"

" me lo dijo."

"¿Cómo lo sabes, 🐤 ?"

"Lo vi con mis propios 👁 👁 . Un ▽ del ☁ se me ⌐ en 🙂 . Le digo

la verdad."

🦊 thought a little, and then calmly dijo: "Don't be afraid. No tengan miedo.

I'll save you all. Come with me, all of you … Vengan conmigo, todos ustedes.

Vengan conmigo a mi 🕳 ."

Then 🦃 , 🦢 , 🦆 , 🐔 y little 🐤 went con 🦊 into her 🕳 .

What happened after that no one sabe for sure. We only sabemos que 🦃 ,

🦢 , 🦆 , 🐔 y little 🐤 never came out de 🕳 de 🦊 .

What do you think happened to them en 🕳 ? Do you think … ¿crees tú que la

🦊 killed them and ate them all?

That's what I think. Creo que la 🦊 los mató y se los comió a todos.

Poor things. ¡Pobrecitos!

🔊 **Turn the audio off.**

## PERFORMANCE CHALLENGE:

There are four parts to this Performance Challenge:
1. Read the story silently to yourself.
2. Read the story aloud to yourself.
3. Read the story aloud to a parent, friend or one of your brothers and sisters.
4. Retell the story in your own words, using as much Spanish as you can, to a parent, friend or one of your brothers or sisters. Don't worry if you can't remember every word. Do the best you can, and review the audio if you need to.

# Chicken Little II

## (Story Telling)

 **Turn the audio on:**

**Tony:** All Right. "El cielo se cae" means "the sky is falling." Right?

**Lisa:** Right. So, how does that help us?

**Tony:** Oh, I'm not sure.

**Lisa:** I know. Let's tell the story to each other again, using as much Spanish as we can remember. That really helped me last time.

*Retell the following story in your own words, using as much Spanish as possible. Use the pictures to remember the words you have learned.*

**Turn the audio off.**

**Note: pause the audio while you tell the story**

**76**

# Word Puzzle 3

*(Chicken Little)*

**6**
*Track18*

🔊 **Turn the audio on.**

**Tony:** Good. And it gave me an idea. When "el pollito" thought that the sky was falling, it was really a leaf from above his head.

**Lisa:** Yeah... so it would make sense if the clue was above our heads!

**Narrator:** You both look above you and see a small ledge. With much stretching, you manage to reach up to the ledge above you and retrieve a piece of parchment.

**Tony:** It looks like a puzzle. We need the words from *El Pollito*.

**Lisa:** Let's hurry up and do it. We don't have much time left to find Grandpa Glen.

🔊 **Turn the audio off.**

*Fill in the blanks in the puzzle below by following the numbered clues. The letters that fall in the circled blanks will make an additional word that will help you on your adventure.*

**1.**

**2.**

**3. Big**

**4. I am**

**5.**

**6. You know**

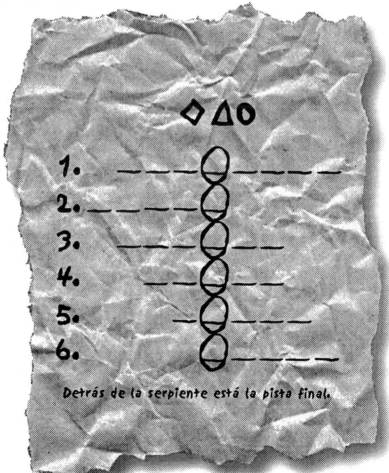

Detrás de la serpiente está la pista final.

**Turn the audio on.**

**Tony:** I don't know what "mantis" is. What's that, on the bottom of the sheet?

**Lisa:** It looks like another riddle. "Detrás de la serpiente está la pista final."

**Tony:** Great. What does that mean?

 **Turn the audio off.**

# The Mantis and The Butterfly

*(Horseshoe Story)*

 **Turn the audio on.**

*Track 20*

**Lisa:** I don't know. Do you suppose that this clue, "mantis," might lead us to the last clue?

**Tony:** It had better. We only have three hours left to find Grandpa Glen. We should hurry. What does the notebook say about this clue?

**Lisa:** Let me see. Okay. "Having found the riddle that led to the last clue, I once again had to fall back on my knowledge of folklore. This riddle referred to an odd little story, *La mantis y la mariposa.*"

***Listen to this story and read it as you listen. You will soon be able to tell it in Spanish following the pictures.***

*Track 21*

## The Mantis and The Butterfly

*He aquí una casa.*
*He aquí un pátio.*
*En el pátio hay un árbol.*
*En el árbol hay una hoja.*
*En la hoja hay una mariposa.*
*Detrás de la mariposa hay una mantis.*
*Detrás de la mantis hay un pájaro.*
*Detrás del pájaro hay un gato.*
*Detrás del gato hay una serpiente.*
*La serpiente quiere comerse el gato.*
*El gato quiere comerse el pájaro.*
*El pájaro quiere comerse la mantis.*
*La mantis quiere comerse la mariposa.*
*Entonces ¿que sucede?*
*La mariposa ve la mantis y vuela huyendo.*
*La mantis pierde su alimento.*
*El pájaro vuela a otra rama.*
*El gato salta del árbol.*
*La serpiente, arrastrándose, se va.*
*Es bueno que la mariposa vió la mantis.*

 **Turn the audio off.**

### PERFORMANCE CHALLENGE:

Create hand actions to represent the actions in the horseshoe story. (For example: Make up different actions to represent the animals you heard about in the story.) After you have created the actions, perform your mini-play for a parent, friend, or one of your bothers or sisters. Remember to narrate your actions in Spanish and then translate your words if your audience does not understand Spanish.

# The Mantis and The Butterfly

*(Match and Learn)*

**Turn the audio on.**

**Tony:** I recognize the words "serpiente" and the word "mantis." So, the clue has something to do with those words.

**Lisa:** Maybe we should go back and ask Marcela.

**Tony:** That's a good idea. We can go over the story on the way back.

*Look at picture box #1 in your workbook.*

**1.**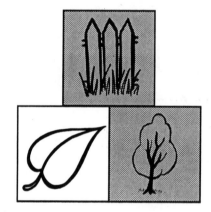

**2.**

**3.**

**4.**

**5.**

**6.**

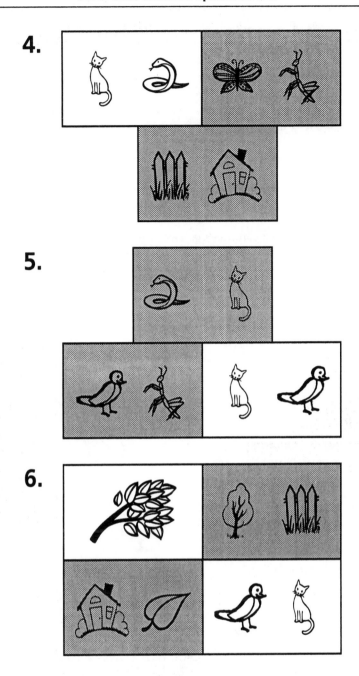

 **Turn the audio off.**

## PERFORMANCE CHALLENGE:

Draw a scene using the pictures you learned in your Match and Learn exercise. After you draw your picture, describe each part of the scene to a parent, friend, or one of your brothers or sisters. Remember to use as much Spanish as you can to talk about your drawing.

# The Mantis and The Butterfly

*(Horseshoe Story Review)*

 **Turn the audio on.**

**Narrator:** Thursday, 10 a.m. You both walk back towards Marcela's house.

**Tony:** Where are we going to find a serpiente? We only have two more hours before we have to go and meet Grandpa Glen. He's going to think that we don't want to come with him!

**Lisa:** Well, we're going as fast as we can. Let's go over the story again and make sure that we know it.

*Listen to this story and read as you listen. You will soon be able to tell it in Spanish following the pictures.*

## The Mantis and The Butterfly

*He aquí una casa.*
*He aquí un pátio.*
*En el pátio hay un árbol.*
*En el árbol hay una hoja.*
*En la hoja hay una mariposa.*
*Detrás de la mariposa hay una mantis.*
*Detrás de la mantis hay un pájaro.*
*Detrás del pájaro hay un gato.*
*Detrás del gato hay una serpiente.*
*La serpiente quiere comerse el gato.*
*El gato quiere comerse el pájaro.*
*El pájaro quiere comerse la mantis.*
*La mantis quiere comerse la mariposa.*
*Entonces ¿que sucede?*
*La mariposa ve la mantis y vuela huyendo.*
*La mantis pierde su alimento.*
*El pájaro vuela a otra rama.*
*El gato salta del árbol.*
*La serpiente, arrastrándose, se va.*
*Es bueno que la mariposa vió la mantis.*

 **Turn the audio off.**

## PERFORMANCE CHALLENGE:

Create hand actions to represent the actions in the horseshoe story. (For example: Make up different actions to represent the animals you heard about in the story.) After you have created the actions, perform your mini-play for a parent, friend, or one of your bothers or sisters. Remember to narrate your actions in Spanish and then translate your words if your audience does not understand Spanish.

# Word Puzzle 4

## *(The Mantis and The Butterfly)*

*Track 26*

 **Turn the audio on.**

**Lisa:** Hey, what's that? Over there, off the road. It looks like a statue.

**Tony:** Yeah, it does. We must've missed it last night in the storm.

**Lisa:** Let's go over and look.

**Narrator:** You go over to the side of the road and look at the statue. It looks Mayan, and it is of many animals all together. Across the bottom is written "MANTIS."

**Lisa:** Quick, quick! Is there a serpiente?

**Tony:** Yes, there is! I see it! And there's a small space underneath it.

**Lisa:** Is there a clue?

**Tony:** Let me see. Yes, it's another puzzle! It needs the words from *La mantis y la mariposa*.

**Turn the audio off.**

Fill in the blanks in the puzzle below by following the numbered clues. The letters that fall in the circled blanks will make additional words that will help you on your adventure.

**1.**

**2.**

**3. He flies**

**4.**

**5.**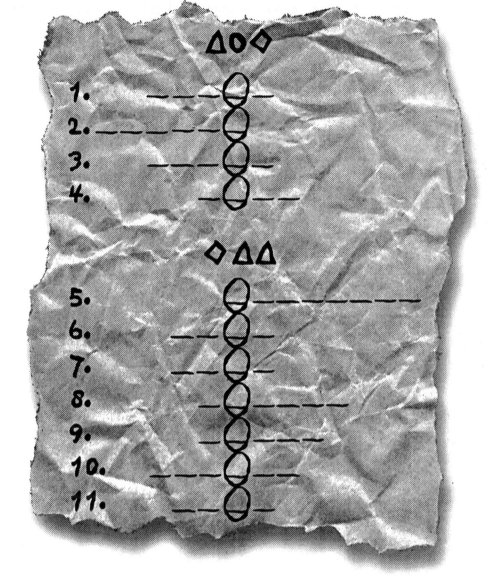

**6. here**

**7.**

**8. behind**

**9.**

**10. he wants**

**11.**

**Turn the audio on.**

**Lisa:** So, what does "Isla Mujeres" mean?

**Tony:** I don't know. We should go back to Marcela's house, I think we need her help.

**Turn the audio off.**

# Final Word Puzzle

*(The Hidden Clue)*

 **Turn the audio on.**

 **6** *Track 28*

**Narrator:** Thursday, 11 a.m. You all arrive breathless at Marcela's house, and you take out all of the puzzles you've done so far.

**Tony:** Okay, what now?

**Lisa:** Yeah, and what about this main puzzle that Grandpa Glen sent us? Look, do you see these shapes next to each line? There's shapes like that in all of the answers to the other puzzles (see pages 37, 45, 77, and 85). I bet if we put those words into Grandpa's puzzle, we could figure out what to do from there.

**Lisa:** Okay. It's worth a try.

 **Turn the audio off.**

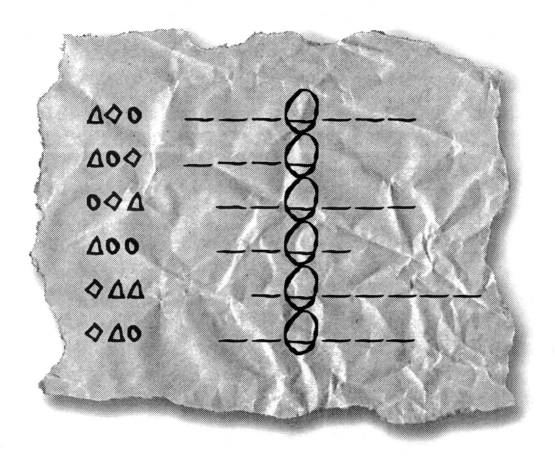

---

**Turn the audio on.**

**Tony:** Okay, it spells "Cancún." Let's look on the map. Can you find a place called Cancún?

**Lisa:** Yes, it's right here. Wow, it's huge! How will we ever find Grandpa Glen in time?

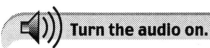 **Turn the audio off.**

# Grandpa!

## (The Reunion)

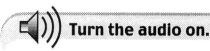 

**Tony:** Look, Lisa! Here! Right off of Cancún is an island called "Isla Mujeres." That must be where Grandpa Glen is going! We have to hurry! We only have an hour left!

**Narrator:** However, at that very moment, who should arrive at Marcela's house but your parents. Concerned by how long you had all been gone, they have come to get you. You tell them everything that has been happening. Your parents are excited, they hadn't had any luck finding Grandpa Glen. They agree to take you to the ferry docks that go between Cancún and Isla Mujeres. Guess who was waiting there?

**Grandpa Glen:** Hi, you guys! I was afraid that you wouldn't make it.

**Lisa:** Grandpa Glen! I'm so glad we found you! Can we go with you to Isla Mujeres?

**Grandpa Glen:** Of course. I need to find that treasure, you know. I can't let Malo find it first. I bought two extra tickets.

**Narrator:** At that moment, however, your parents interrupt and object. They aren't exactly sure what is going on but are afraid it might be too dangerous for children to be involved in.

**Tony:** But, Mom! Dad! We've learned so much!

**Lisa:** Yes, and our Spanish has gotten so much better!

**Narrator:** Your mother and father exchange looks, and say that if you can really prove how much Spanish you have learned, and they are sufficiently impressed, that they will let you go to Isla Mujeres with your grandfather. You take a deep breath.

 **Turn the audio off.**

# Test 2

### (Review)

  **Turn the audio on.**

*Track 31* A. Frame Identifications

*For each question, you will see a box with pictures. You will hear a statement about one of the pictures. There will be a pause of 10 seconds to identify the picture, and then the statement will be repeated.*

**1.**

**2.**

**3.**

**4.**

**5.**

## Comprehension Multiple-Choice

*Complete the following conversations by choosing the correct answer from the options listed.*

1. Uno, dos, tres, cuatro, cinco, seis...
   What comes next?

   A. ocho.

   B. diez

   C. siete

   D. nueve

2. "Pollito, pollito, you say the sky se está cayendo.
   ¿Cómo lo sabes?"

   A. No sé cómo.

   B. La gallina told me so.

   C. El cochinito fell on my cabeza!

   D. I saw it con mis propios ojos!

3. Whose idea was it to go into la cueva?

   A. El elefante.

   B. La zorra

   C. El pato.

   D. La mantis

4. Which of the following are insects?

   A. El pájaro y la serpiente.

   B. La hoja y el cielo.

   C. El pátio y el árbol.

   D. La mantis y la mariposa.

5. How would you say "Here I am" in Spanish?

   A. Aquí estoy.

   B. ¡Hasta luego!

   C. Muy bien, gracias.

   D. Chao pues.

*Now go on to complete the reading/writing portion of this test.*

 **Turn the audio off.**

## Matching

*Choose the statements that match and draw a line to connect the two.*

1. butterfly

2. cave

3. tree

4. mouse

5. yard

A. ratón

B. mariposa

C. patio

D. cueva

E. árbol

## True or False

*Write T or F for each statement.*

_____ 1. Un pavo muy grande fell on chickie's cabeza.

_____ 2. El pollito thought the sky se está cayendo.

_____ 3. Los animales asked chickie, "¿Cómo lo sabes?"

_____ 4. El pollito responded, "Aquí estoy."

_____ 5. La gallina told los animales, "Corran, Corran!"

# Answer Key

**1.**

**2.**

**3.**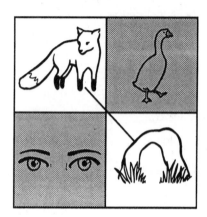

**4.**

**5.**

**Comprehension Multiple-Choice**

1. C. siete

2. D. I saw it con mis propios ojos!

3. B. La zorra

4. D. La mantis y la mariposa

5. A. Aquí estoy

**Matching**

1. B

2. D

3. E

4. A

5. C

**True or False**

1. F

2. T

3. T

4. F

5. F